3-D Christian Story Sta.

Shape and three-dimensional books, by being tangible and requiring creative involvement, excite and motivate children to write. Each of the book themes is designed to inspire children to explore and express their thoughts and ideas. When completed, each book becomes a published work written in the child's own very important and special words.

General Information

- Read over the directions for the book your students will be making ahead of time. Make a sample of the book to show the students what they will be making. Adjust any procedures to meet the needs and abilities of your students.

- Write the vocabulary word suggestions on the chalkboard or chart paper. These are only suggestions and you may want to select only the words that would be most appropriate for your students. Encourage the students to suggest words to add to the list.

- The listed story ideas are only a starting point. Brainstorm ideas as a class and encourage students to come up with their own ideas.

- Have the students write and edit their stories on scratch paper first. Then, have them make the shape or three-dimensional book and copy their stories on the appropriate paper.

- Directions indicate using writing paper. If you wish, students may instead write on the blank section below the picture portion or on the inside of the book.

Use the shape and three-dimensional patterns . . .

- as they are presented to make a variety of shape and three-dimensional books.

- to make a class big book by enlarging the patterns to the size you need. Then, enjoy writing a story together as a class.

- to make basic shape books. Enlarge the pattern you wish to use. Then, simply make a copy of the enlarged pattern on construction paper. Students cut out the shape and write their stories on the back.

- to make basic shape books with the story pages between a front and back cover. Enlarge the pattern you wish to use. Trace the outline of the enlarged pattern. Then, make one copy of the outline pattern on construction paper and several copies on lined writing paper. Students cut out all shape pages. Insert the writing sheets between the cover pages and staple together along the top or left side.

Together may you and your students share the excitement of writing and creating books!

Genesis 2–3

Teacher Preparation for Each Student:

- Make a copy of the Garden of Eden patterns (pages 3 and 4) on white construction paper.
- Cut writing paper into 4-by-8½-inch sheets.

Student Instructions:

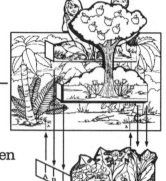

1. Color all pictures. Then, cut out each picture along the solid outer lines.

2. Cut slits where indicated by solid lines.

3. Fold along the dotted lines.

4. Insert the front flower and plant section (A) into the garden background piece. Fold over the tabs and glue in place.

5. Insert the Adam and Eve section (B) into the slits (B) in front of the background. Fold over the tabs and glue in place.

6. Insert the apple tree section (C) into the slits (C) in front of the Adam and Eve section. Fold over the tabs and glue in place.

7. Fold a sheet of 9-by-12-inch construction paper in half. Open it.

8. Glue the background piece to the inside of the top half of the construction paper, being sure that the bottom edge is along the fold line.

9. Copy your story on the writing paper.

10. Arrange your story pages in order, placing the first page of the story on top.

11. Glue the last page of the story to the bottom section below the three-dimensional picture. Place the other pages on top of the last page and staple them all to the book along the left side.

12. As you fold the top down, gently pull the pop-out section to one side.

13. Write the story title and your name on the front cover.

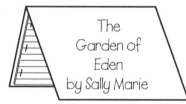

The Garden of Eden by Sally Marie

Vocabulary Suggestions

God	creation	created	rib	land	evil
naked	plants	trees	eat	die	apple
banished	rivers	animals	man	woman	good
garden	Eden	Adam	Eve	serpent	
temptation	knowledge	naming			

Writing Ideas

- The Story of the Garden of Eden
- Write a description of the Garden of Eden.
- Imagine you were Adam or Eve and write about your life in the Garden of Eden.

- Write what you think would be the ideal, or perfect, place to live in today's world.
- I think a serpent was chosen to tempt Adam and Eve because . . .
- If Adam and Eve had never eaten the fruit, then . . .

Genesis 6:5–22; 7; 8; 9:1–17

Teacher Preparation for Each Student:

- Make a copy of the Noah and the Ark patterns (pages 6 and 7) on white construction paper.
- Cut writing paper into 5-by-8-inch sheets.

Student Instructions:

1. Color Noah, the animals, and the ark.
2. Cut out Noah, the animals, the ark, and the tabs along the solid outer lines.
3. Fold the tabs accordion-style along the dotted lines.
4. Glue Noah and the animals each to an end of a tab.
5. Glue the loose end of each tab to the ark background scene.
6. Copy your story on the writing paper.
7. Arrange your story pages in order, placing the first page on top.

8. Glue the last page of your story in the space at the bottom below the ark scene.
9. Place the other pages on top and staple along the left side.
10. Fold the book in half along the dotted center line.
11. Fold a sheet of 9-by-12-inch colored construction paper in half to make a cover. Glue the picture/story page to the inside cover, matching the fold lines.
12. Close the book. Write the story title and your name on the front cover.

God Sends
a Flood
by Tyrone Smith

Vocabulary Suggestions

people	evil	wicked	God	obeyed
destroy	man	beast	Noah	build
ark	three	decks	window	door
wife	sons	family	two	animals
living things	food	rain	flood	forty
days	nights	birds	sign	raven
rainbow	dove	covenant	promise	altar

Writing Ideas

- Write about life on the ark, pretending you were one of Noah's sons or daughters-in-law.
- Write about some of the animals you would have put in the ark and the food they would have needed.

- A Flood
- What God's Promise Means to Me
- A New Beginning for Humankind

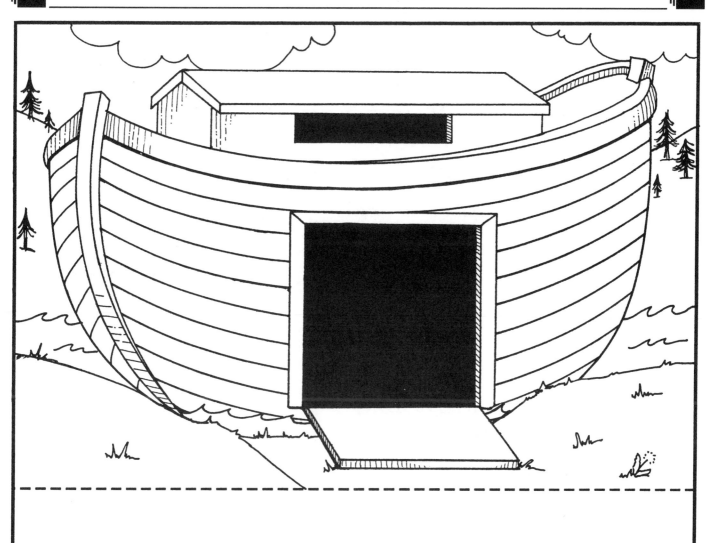

Paste
story
here.

Genesis 9:8–17

Teacher Preparation for Each Student:

- Make a copy of the cloud and rainbow patterns (page 9) on white construction paper.
- Cut writing paper into 5½-by-8½-inch sheets.

Student Instructions:

1. Color and cut out the rainbow and cloud along the solid outer lines.

2. Cut slits on the two solid lines on the cloud.

3. Fold the tabs on the rainbow and insert them into the slits on the cloud. Glue the tabs in place to the back of the cloud.

Cut

4. To make the book cover, fold a sheet of 9-by-12-inch colored construction paper in half. Open it.

5. Glue the cloud to the inside of the top half of the construction paper.

6. Copy your story on the writing paper.

7. Arrange your story pages in order, placing the first page on top.

8. Glue the last page of your story in the space below the cloud picture.

9. Place the other pages on top and staple to the book along the left side.

10. Close your book. Write the story title and your name on the front cover.

Vocabulary Suggestions

rainbow	make	promises	God	ark	Noah
covenant	red	reminder	sign	clouds	remind
everlasting	living	creature	earth	over	token
between	colors	color	arc	sky	heaven
remember	yellow	blue	green	purple	pink

Writing Ideas

- After the Flood
- When I see a rainbow, I . . .
- My Promise to God
- God's Promises

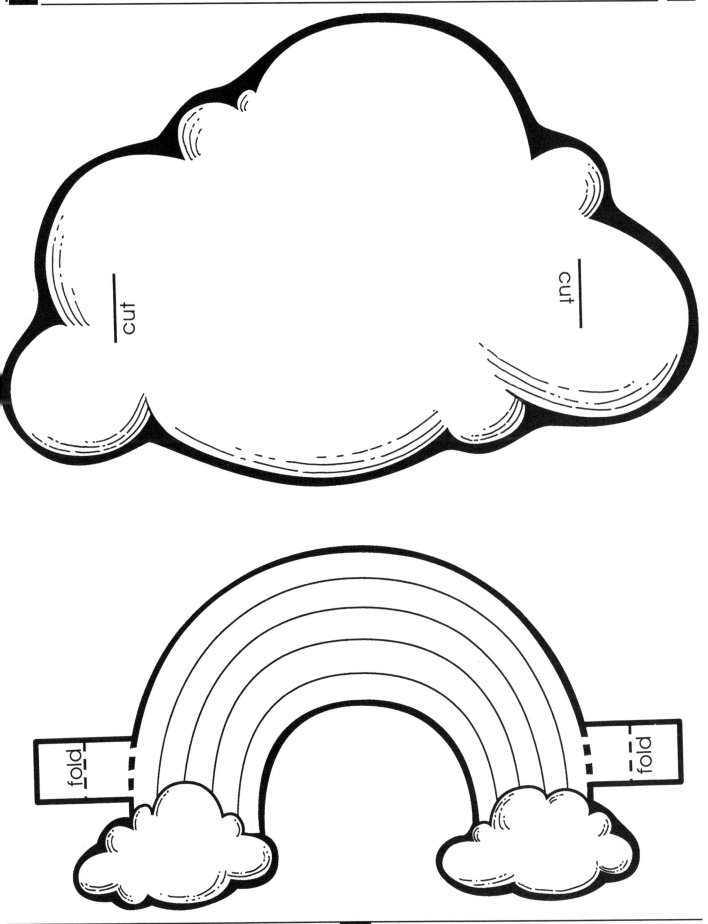

cut

cut

fold

fold

Genesis 37

Teacher Preparation for Each Student:

- Make a copy of the Joseph patterns (pages 11 and 12) on white construction paper.
- Cut writing paper into 3½-by-4-inch sheets.

Student Instructions:

1. Cut out all pieces along the solid outer lines.
2. Fold the side sections of the upper body along the dotted lines.

3. Glue the head to the tab at the top of the body.

4. Glue the tabs on the arms to the back of the body.

5. Copy your story on the writing paper.

6. Put the story pages in order, placing the first page on top.
7. Open the robe flaps. Place the story pages inside. Then, staple them to the body along the top edge below the neck.
8. Write the story title and your name on the inside flaps.
9. Close the flaps of the robe. Draw stripes on the robe. Color Joseph.

Vocabulary Suggestions

Joseph	Jacob	father	son	seventeen
loved	most	coat	colors	colorful
stripes	brothers	jealous	jealousy	envious
envy	dream	mean	mourned	sheep
flocks	plotted	sold	merchants	pit
traders	silver	Egypt	goat	lie
blood				

Writing Ideas

- Sold by His Brothers
- Joseph's Dreams
- The Special Coat
- Jealousy is . . .

- Joseph's brothers were angry because . . .
- Write about what Joseph might have been thinking while down in the pit.

Tab

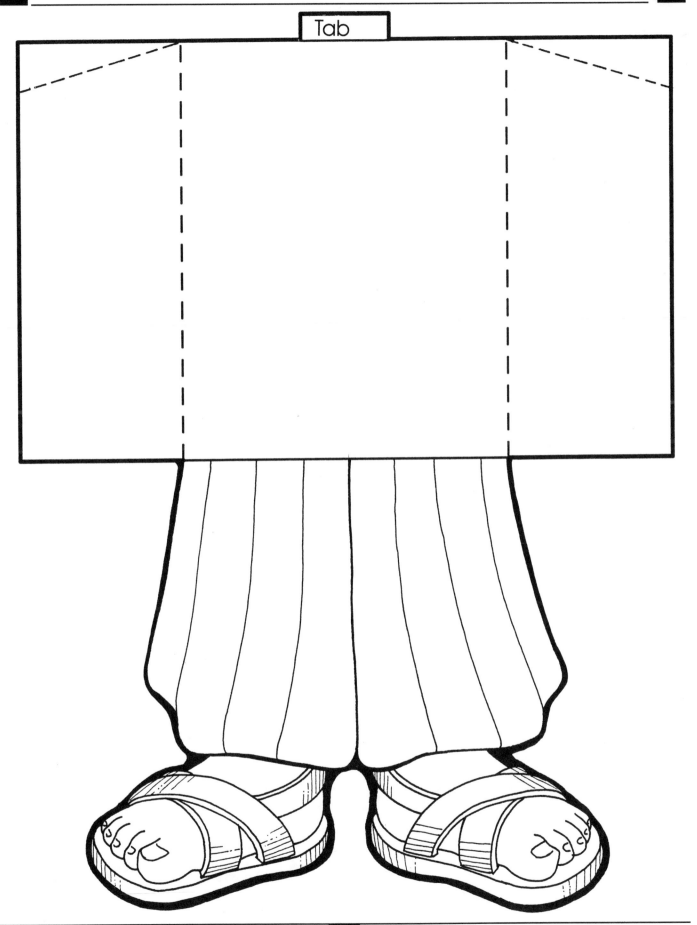

Exodus 1; 2:1–10

Teacher Preparation for Each Student:

- Make a copy of the baby Moses patterns (page 14) on white construction paper.

- Trace the outline of the front of baby Moses on white paper. Draw a margin line one-half inch in from the left edge on the outline.

- Make several copies of the outline on lined writing paper.

- Make two copies of the basket pattern (page 15) on yellow, tan, or brown construction paper.

Student Instructions:

1. Cut out all shape pages, including lined writing pages.

2. Copy your story on the lined writing pages.

3. Put your story pages in order. Insert them between the baby Moses cover pages. Staple them together along the left side.

leave open

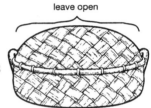

4. Write the story title and your name on the front cover of the baby Moses book.

5. Glue the front and back covers of the basket together along the side and bottom edges. Begin and end at the bottom of the lid. Leave the top lid section open to make a "pocket."

6. Put your completed baby Moses book inside the basket.

Vocabulary Suggestions

Egyptians	Pharaoh	ruler	king	many
Hebrew	papyrus	mighty	live	child
forced	work	kill	boys	girls
children of Israel	hid	Levi	wife	reeds
midwives	three	months	wove	basket
bulrushes	pitch	river	son	saw
taskmasters	tar	maids	Moses	pity
daughter	crying	sister	baby	

Writing Ideas

- When I opened the basket and saw a baby, I . . .

- I think that it is okay to disobey a law if . . .

- Moses was a good name for the baby because . . .

- Imagine you were a baby put in a basket and set in a river. Write how you would feel.

- God Protects Moses

- A Kind Daughter

- Imagine you were the Pharaoh's daughter. Write what you would say to the Pharaoh about saving and then adopting Moses.

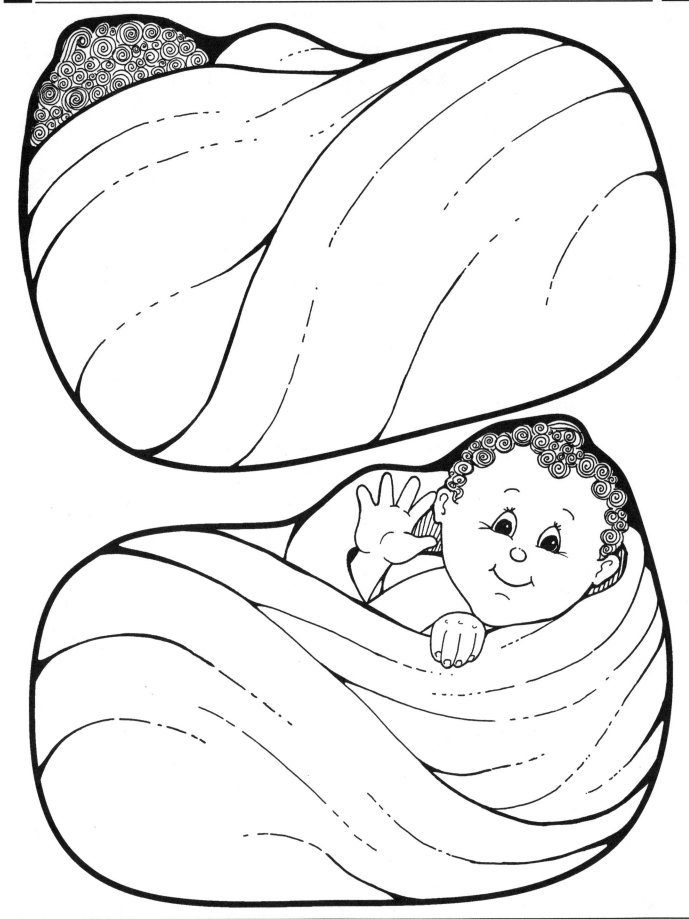

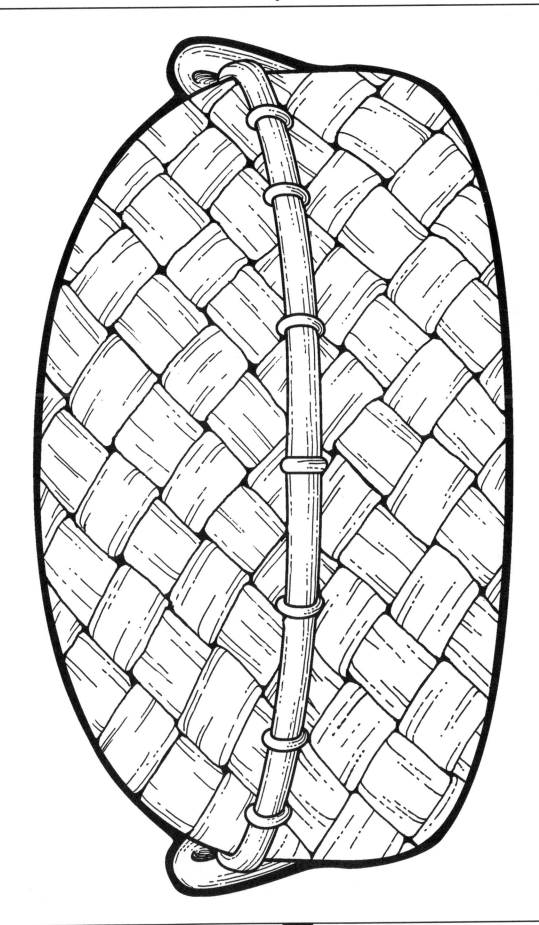

Exodus 7; 8; 9; 10; 11; 12:1–30

Teacher Preparation for Each Student:

- Make a copy of the Pharaoh patterns (pages 17 and 18) on white construction paper.
- Cut writing paper into 3½-by-4-inch sheets.

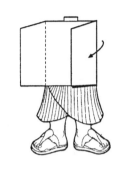

Student Instructions:

1. Cut out all shape pieces along the solid outer lines.
2. Fold the side sections of the upper body toward the center along the dotted lines.
3. Glue the head to the tab at the top of the body.
4. Glue the tabs on the arms to the back of the body.
5. Glue the belt pieces along the bottom of the flaps.
6. Glue the collar pieces along the top of the flaps.
7. Copy your story on the writing paper.
8. Put your story pages in order, placing the first page on top.
9. Open the jacket flaps. Place the story pages inside. Then, staple them to the body along the top edge.
10. Write the title and your name on the inside flaps.
11. Close the jacket flaps. Color Pharaoh.

Vocabulary Suggestions

Pharaoh	frogs	plagues	flies	miracle
Moses	Aaron	believe	God	boils/sores
blood	leave	magicians	serpents	Passover
Egypt	gnats	swarms	Egyptians	livestock
river	hail	door frames	locusts	darkness
summon	days	firstborn	servants	freedom
worship	rod	threaten	Israelites	Hebrews

Writing Ideas

- If I had been Pharaoh, I would have let the people leave when . . .
- Of all the plagues on Egypt, I think the worst was . . . because . . .
- Pretend you are an Egyptian and write about experiencing the plagues.
- I would/would not have liked being an Egyptian pharaoh because . . .

- Imagine you were Moses. How would you have convinced the Pharaoh to let your people leave Egypt?

To the Teacher

Option: *Students may also use this pharaoh when studying Joseph and the Pharaoh, Genesis 41 and 47. Create your own writing ideas and vocabulary lists.*

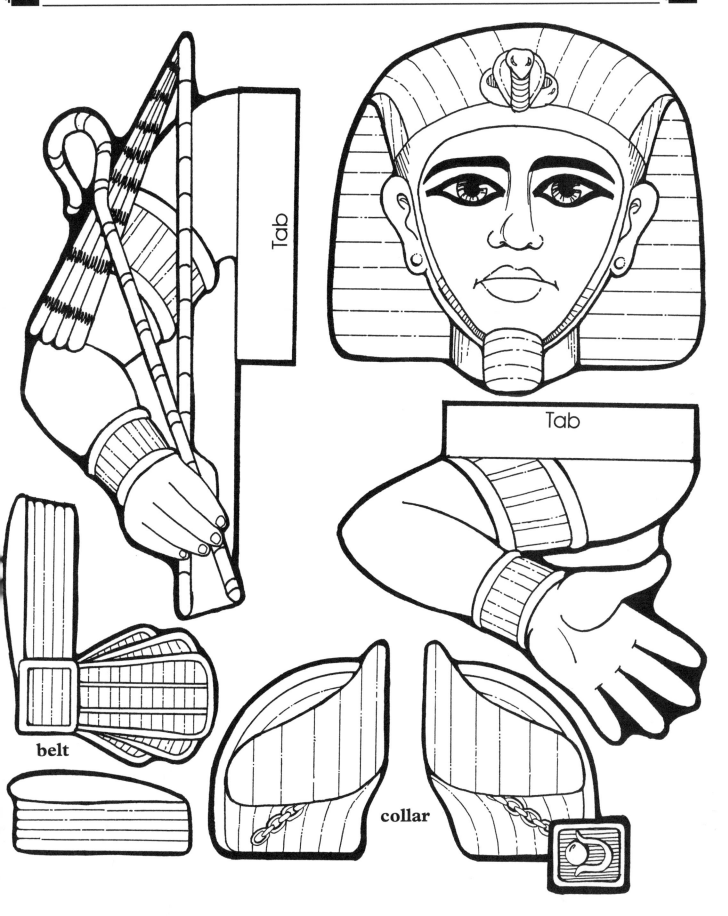

belt

collar

Tab

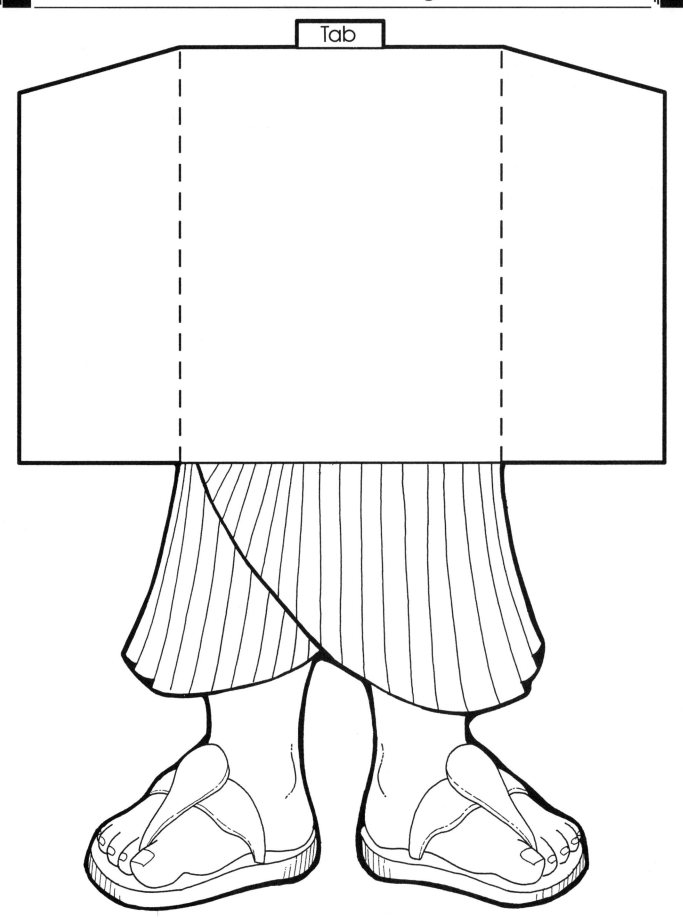

Exodus 19; 20:1–21; 32:1–35; 34:1–4, 28; Deuteronomy 5:1–22

Teacher Preparation for Each Student:

- Duplicate the Ten Commandments patterns (pages 20 and 21) on gray construction paper.
- Cut writing paper into 5-by-7½-inch sheets. Make sure there is at least one-half inch of unlined space at the top.

Student draws here.

Student Instructions:

1. Cut out all shape pages along the solid outer lines.
2. Copy your story on the writing paper.
3. Draw and color an illustration of your story in the blank space on the background.

4. Place the story pages in order on top of your illustration. Staple them to the background along the top edge.

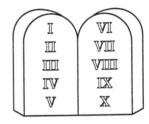

5. Place the front tablets of the Ten Commandments on top of your story.

6. Staple each of the front tablets to the background piece along the sides.
7. Open the covers and write the story title and your name on the inside of the covers.
8. Close the covers and color the numbers on the front of the tablets.

Vocabulary Suggestions

Moses	God	no	Sabbath	gods
graven	images	name	Sunday	other
mountain	honor	parents	commit	kill
adultery	steal	lie	misuse	ten
desire/covet	holy	fire		

Writing Ideas

- Moses and the Ten Commandments
- Choose one commandment and write why you think God made this rule.
- If everyone followed the Ten Commandments, the world would . . .
- When someone tells a lie, . . .
- Stealing is . . .

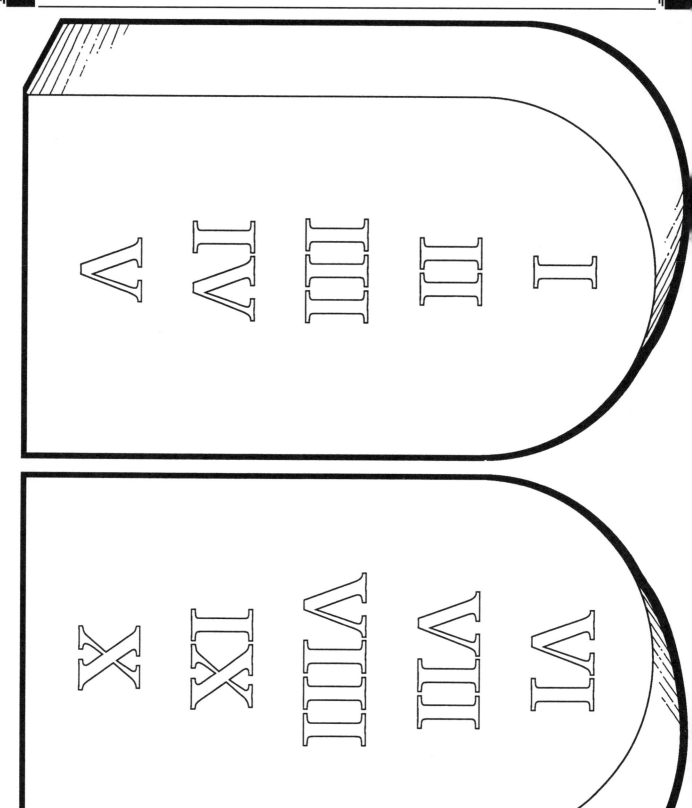

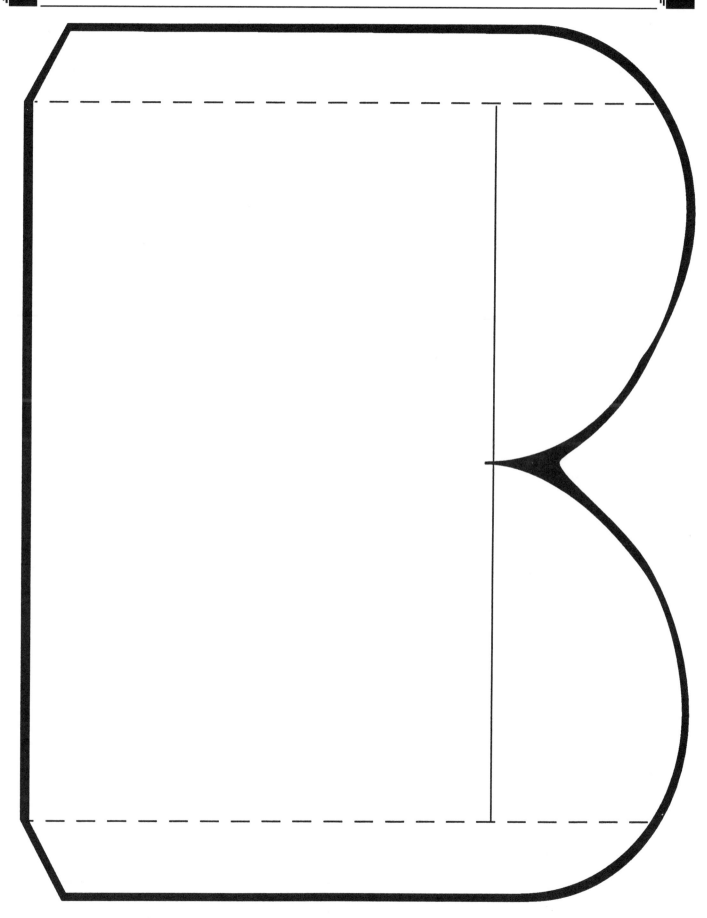

Samson at the Temple

Judges 16:4–31

Teacher Preparation for Each Student:

- Duplicate the Samson at the Temple patterns (page 23) on white construction paper.
- Cut writing paper into 5½-by-8½-inch sheets.

— Cut

Student Instructions:

1. Color and cut out the pillars and Samson background scene along the solid outer lines.

2. Cut four slits on the marked lines on the Samson background scene.

3. Fold the tabs on the pillars and insert them into the slits on the Samson background scene. Glue the tabs in place to the back of the Samson background scene.

4. Fold a sheet of 9-by-12-inch construction paper in half for a cover. Open it.

5. Glue the Samson picture to the inside of the top half of the construction paper.

6. Copy your story on the writing paper.

7. Arrange your story pages in order, placing the first page on top.

8. Glue the last page of your story to the space below the Samson picture.

9. Place the other pages on top and staple to the book along the left side.

10. Close your book. Write the story title and your name on the front cover.

Vocabulary Suggestions

Samson	Delilah	strength	strong	pushed
shekels	Philistines	shackles	might	silver
weak	helpless	temple	waiting	secret
killed	ropes	bound	tie	locks
hair	razor	shave	sleep	blinded
prison	Gaza	grow	pillars	revenge
betray	tumble			

Writing Ideas

- Betrayed by a Friend
- Samson was strong because . . .
- Write about what gives you strength, either physically or spiritually.
- Before Samson told Delilah his secret, he fooled her three times . . .

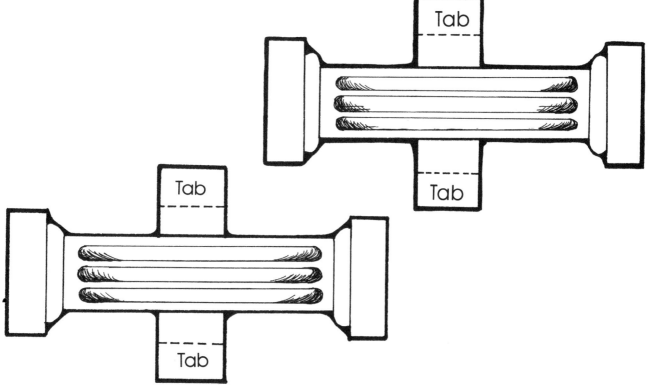

1 Samuel 17

Teacher Preparation for Each Student:

- Duplicate the battlefield background scene, David, Goliath, and the tab patterns (page 25) on white construction paper.
- Cut writing paper into 5-by-8-inch sheets.

Student Instructions:

1. Color the battlefield background scene, David, and Goliath.
2. Cut out David, Goliath, the battlefield background scene, and the tabs along the solid outer lines.
3. Fold the tabs accordion-style along the dotted lines.
4. Glue David to the end of tab A. Glue Goliath to the end of tab B.
5. Glue the loose ends of tabs A and B to the A and B on the battlefield background scene.
6. Fold a sheet of 9-by-12-inch colored construction paper in half for a cover. Open it.
7. Glue the background piece to the inside of the top half of the construction paper.
8. Copy your story on the writing paper.
9. Arrange your story pages in order, placing the first page on top.
10. Glue the last page of your story to the bottom half of the construction paper, below the battlefield scene.
11. Place the other pages on top and staple along the left side.
12. Close the book. Write the story title and your name on the front cover.

Vocabulary Suggestions

Saul	Israel	Philistines	David	Goliath
giant	fight	champion	battle	battlefield
helmet	armor	protect	sword	brothers
food	afraid	youngest	son	challenge
spear	five	stones	sling	forehead
fled	armies	brave	Lord	boy
staff				

Writing Ideas

- God Was with David
- Size Does Not Mean Power
- If I were David, I . . .

- Imagine David were your brother. Write how you would feel as you watched him prepare to battle the giant Goliath.

Daniel 3

Teacher Preparation for Each Student:

- Duplicate the Three Men in a Furnace patterns (pages 27 and 28) on white construction paper.
- Cut writing paper into 4-by-8½-inch sheets.

Student Instructions:

1. Color all of the pictures. Then, cut out each picture along the solid outer line.
2. Cut slits indicated by solid lines.
3. Fold along the dotted lines.
4. Insert slit A of the front furnace section (A) into slit A of the background piece. Fold over the tabs and glue in place.

5. Insert the three men section (B) into the B slits of the furnace section. Fold over the tabs and glue in place.
6. Insert the flames section (C) into the C slits of the furnace section. Fold over the tabs and glue in place.
7. Fold a sheet of 9-by-12-inch colored construction paper in half. Open it.
8. Glue the background piece to the inside of the top half of the construction paper, placing the bottom edge along the fold line.
9. Copy your story on the writing paper.
10. Arrange the story pages in order, with the first page of the story on top.
11. Glue the last page of the story to the bottom section of the construction paper below the three-dimensional picture. Place the other pages on top and staple to the book along the left side.

Trusting in God

by Suzanne Alexander

12. As you fold the top down, gently pull the pop-out section to one side.
13. Write the story title and your name on the front cover.

Vocabulary Suggestions

Nebuchadnezzar	tied	angel	officials	statue
gold	hear	music	horn	flute
harp	decree	law	down	worship
rescue	throw	furnace	burning	fiery
Shadrach	Meshach	Abednego	scorched	refuse
heat	hot	flame	unharmed	singed
live	faith	trust	protect	believe

Writing Ideas

- Write a letter to Nebuchadnezzar explaining why you would not fall down and worship the golden statue.
- Trusting in God
- Only One God
- Write the story of the Three Men in a Furnace from King Nebuchadnezzar's point of view.

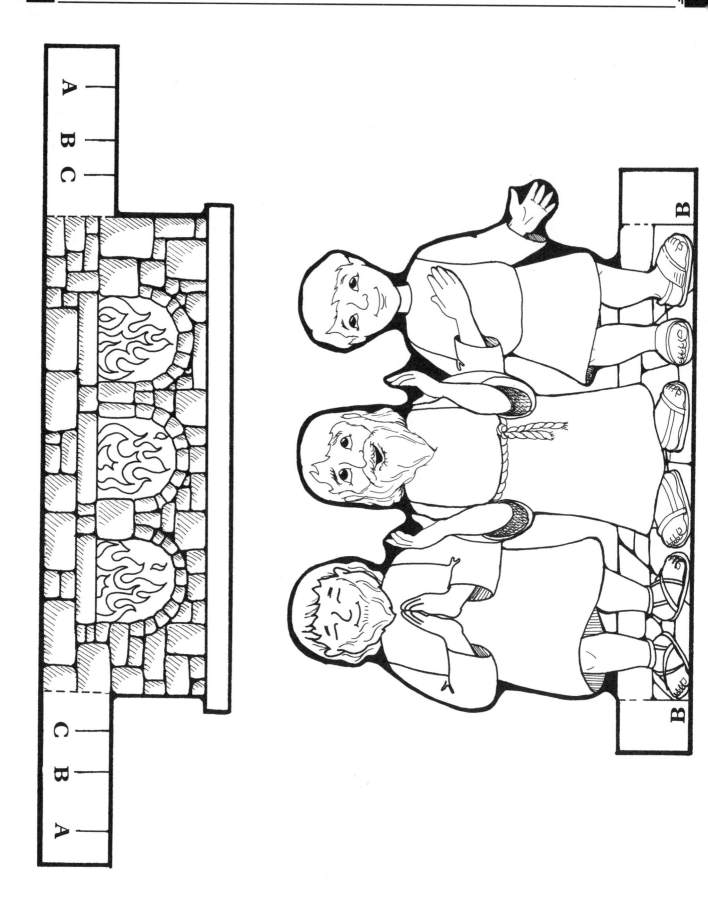

Daniel 6

Teacher Preparation for Each Student:

- Duplicate the lions' den background scene, the lions, and the tab patterns (page 30) on white construction paper.
- Cut writing paper into 5-by-8-inch sheets.

Student Instructions:

1. Color the lions' den background scene and the lions.
2. Cut out the lions' den background scene, the lions, and the tabs along the solid outer lines.
3. Fold the tabs accordion-style along the dotted lines.
4. Glue one lion to the end of each tab.
5. Glue the loose end of each tab to the lions' den background scene.
6. Fold a sheet of 9-by-12-inch colored construction paper in half. Open it and glue the picture to the inside of the top half.

7. Copy your story on the writing paper.
8. Arrange your story pages in order, placing the first page on top.

9. Glue the last page of your story to the bottom half of the construction paper, below the lions' den scene.
10. Place the other pages on top and staple along the left side.
11. Close the book. Write the story title and your name on the front cover.

Vocabulary Suggestions

King Darius	kingdom	presidents	Daniel	boss
find	fault	faithful	loyal	law
thrown	den	lions	any	god
thirty	days	decree	three	times
daily	pray	give	thanks	night
prayed	morning	saw	closed	mouths
hurt	unharmed	believe	God	rescue
save	truthful	trust	governors	advisers

Writing Ideas

- Faithfulness and Loyalty Are Rewarded
- Imagine you were Daniel. Describe how you felt when you were thrown into the den of lions.

- Why Others Wanted to Harm Daniel
- It is sometimes okay to disobey a law. . . .
- Imagine you were one of the lions. Write the story from its perspective.

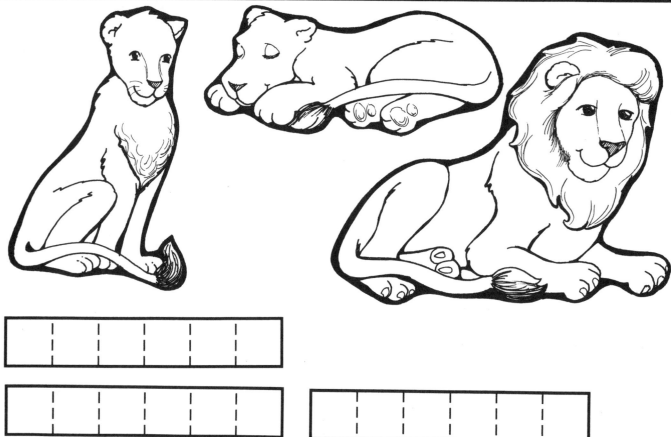

Jonah 1 and 2

Teacher Preparation for Each Student:

- Duplicate the Jonah patterns (page 32) on white construction paper.

- Trace the outline of the Jonah pattern on white paper. Draw a margin line one-half inch down from the top edge of the Jonah outline.

- Make several copies of the outline on lined writing paper.

- Make a copy of the whale patterns (pages 33 and 34) on gray construction paper.

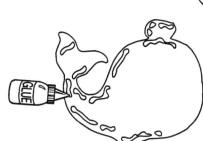

Student Instructions:

1. Cut out all shape pages.

2. Copy your story on the lined writing pages.

3. Put your story pages in order. Insert them between the Jonah cover pages. Staple them together along the top edge.

4. Write the story title and your name on the front of the whale.

5. Glue the front and back whale sections together along the top, tail, and bottom edges. Leave the front open to make a "pocket."

6. Store your completed Jonah book inside the whale.

leave open

God Used a Whale By Sharon Brown

Vocabulary Suggestions

Jonah	Lord	preach	sacrifice	ship
sea	wind	sailors	afraid	danger
overboard	cargo	threw	punish	blame
fault	cause	lighten	captain	escape
ran away	calm	throw	stopped	out
great fish	whale	swallow	three	days
nights	stomach	belly	pray	land
vomited	wickedness	Nineveh		

Writing Ideas

- The storm was rocking the ship violently, and I knew it was because of me . . .

- Imagine you were Jonah inside the whale. Write a prayer you would say to God.

- Write a story from a sailor's viewpoint, recalling the story of finding Jonah alive.

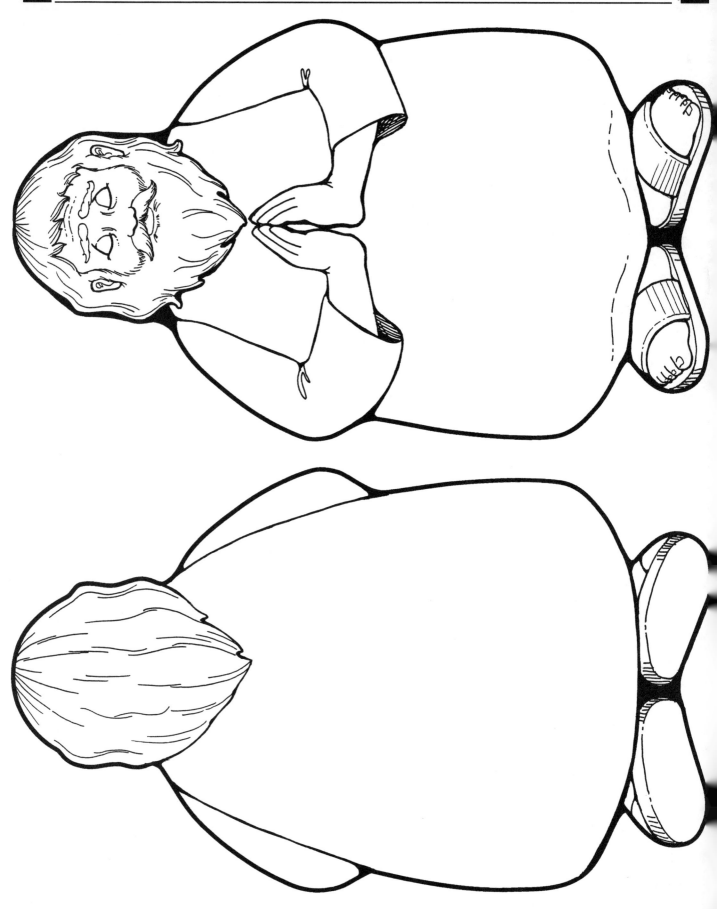

Jonah and the Whale

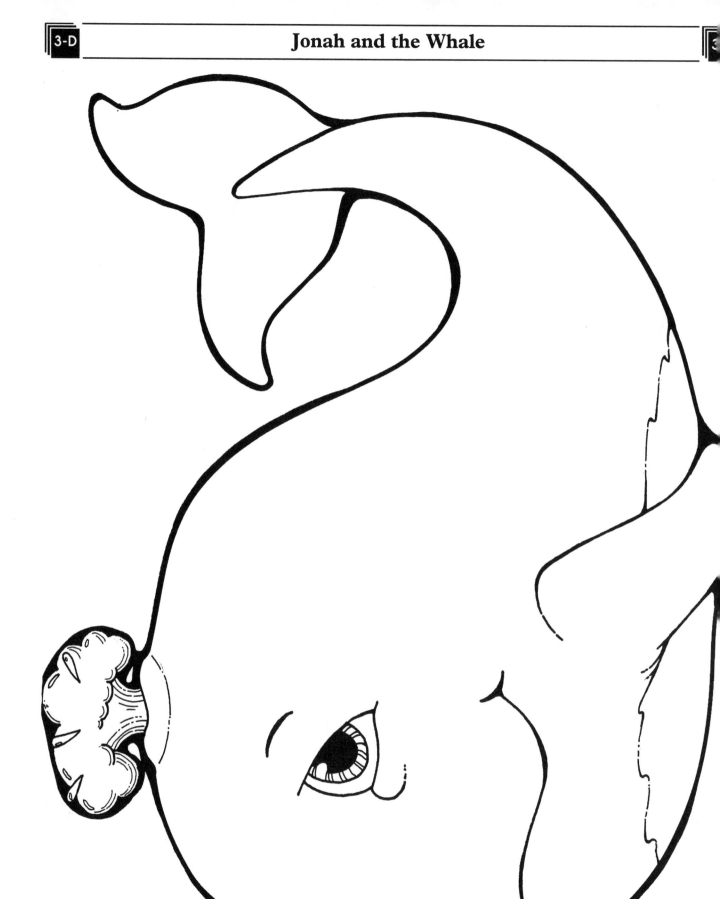

Angel

Luke 1:26–38; Luke 2:8–17; Acts 5:12–42

Teacher Preparation for Each Student:

- Make a copy of the angel patterns (pages 36 and 37) on white construction paper.
- Cut writing paper into 3¾-by-4-inch sheets.

Student Instructions:

1. Cut out all pieces along the solid outer lines.
2. Fold the side sections of the upper body toward the center along the dotted lines.
3. Glue the angel's neck to the tab at the top of the body.
4. Glue the tabs on the wings/arms to the back of the body.
5. Glue the cord belt pieces along the bottom of the front flaps.
6. Copy your story on the writing paper.
7. Put the story pages in order, placing the first page on top.
8. Open the flaps. Place the story pages inside. Then, staple them to the body just below the neck.
9. Write the title and your name on the inside flaps.
10. Close the flaps. Color the angel.

Vocabulary Suggestions

angel	appear	spoke	said	visit
vision	messenger	signs	message	rejoice
prayer	answered	bring	tidings	dream
sky	Gabriel	glory	wings	heaven
help	joy			

Writing Ideas

- The Angel Named Gabriel
- My Guardian Angel
- In my dream an angel appeared and said . . .

- An Angel's Message
- Retell your favorite Bible story that has an angel in it.

Tab

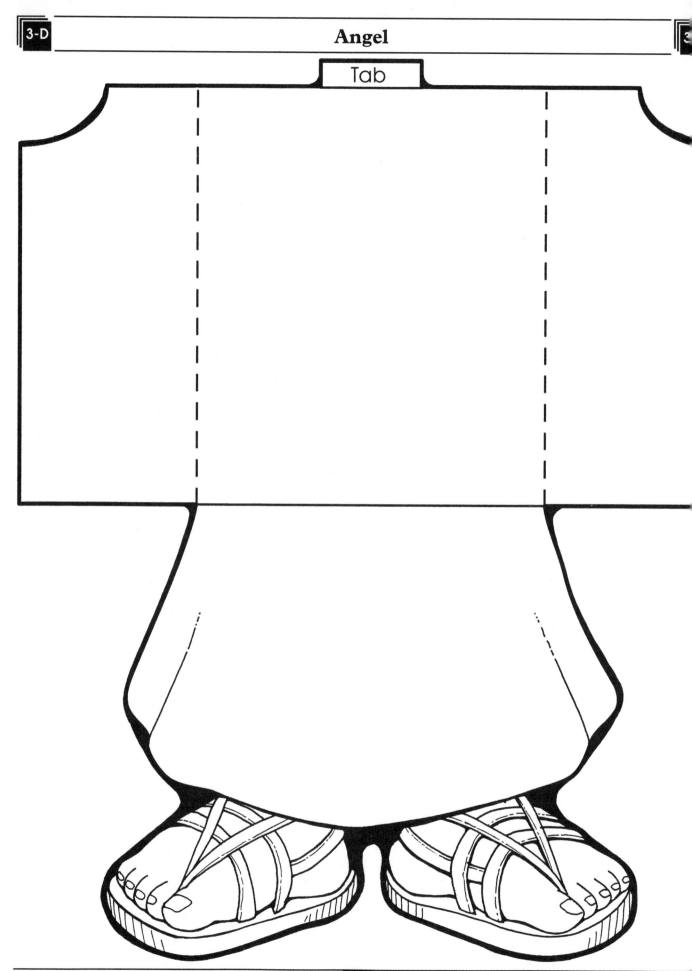

Matthew 1:18–25; 2:1–12; Luke 2:1–20

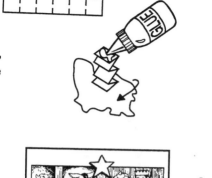

Teacher Preparation for Each Student:

- Duplicate the stable background scene, Mary and Jesus, Joseph, the star, and the tab patterns (page 39) on white construction paper.
- Cut writing paper into 5-by-8-inch sheets.

Student Instructions:

1. Color the stable background scene, Mary and Jesus, Joseph, and the star.
2. Cut out Mary and Jesus, Joseph, the star, the stable background scene, and the tabs along the solid outer lines.
3. Fold the tabs accordion-style along the dotted lines.
4. Glue Mary and Jesus, Joseph, and the star each to an end of a tab.
5. Glue the loose end of each tab to the stable background scene.
6. Fold a sheet of 9-by-12-inch colored construction paper in half for a cover. Open it and glue the picture to the inside of the top half.
7. Copy your story on the writing paper.
8. Arrange your story pages in order, placing the first page on top.
9. Glue the last page of your story to the bottom half of the construction paper, below the stable scene.
10. Place the other pages on top and staple along the left side.
11. Close the book. Write your story title and name on the front cover.

The Story
of Christmas
by Steven Ward

Vocabulary Suggestions

birth	Jesus	Mary	Joseph	inn
stable	taxes	Bethlehem	wrapped	manger
animals	cows	donkey	sheep	shining
bright	star	shepherds	flock	lead
led	angel	wise men	east	search
born	Savior	celebrate	good	news
presents	gold	frankincense	myrrh	wonder
rejoice	peace	Christmas		

Writing Ideas

- Following the Star
- Imagine you were one of the shepherds. Write what you said and felt when you saw baby Jesus lying in the manger.
- Write about a Christmas celebration at your church.

- The wise men brought special gifts to baby Jesus. Write about a gift you woul have brought to baby Jesus and why yo chose it.
- The Journey to Bethlehem
- A Prayer for Baby Jesus

Fishermen

Matthew 4:18–22; 17:24–27; Mark 1:16–20; Luke 5:1–11; John 21:1–14

Teacher Preparation for Each Student:

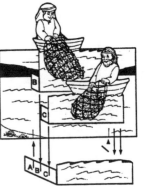

- Duplicate the fishermen scene patterns (pages 41 and 42) on white construction paper.
- Cut writing paper into 4-by-8½-inch sheets.

Student Instructions:

1. Color all of the pictures. Then, cut out each picture along the solid outer line.
2. Cut slits indicated by solid lines.
3. Fold along the dotted lines.
4. Insert the A slits from the front water section into the A slits of the background scene. Fold over the tabs and glue in place.
5. Insert fisherman B into the B slits in the water section. Fold over the tabs and glue in place.
6. Insert fisherman C into the C slits of the water section. Fold over the tabs and glue in place.
7. Fold a sheet of 9-by-12-inch colored construction paper in half for a cover. Open it.
8. Glue the background piece to the inside of the top half, placing the bottom edge along the fold line.
9. Copy your story on the writing paper.
10. Arrange your story pages in order with the first page on top.
11. Glue the last page of the story to the construction paper below the three-dimensional picture. Place the other pages on top and staple to the book along the left side.
12. As you fold the top down, gently pull the pop-out section to one side.
13. Write your story title and name on the front cover.

The Miracle of the Fish

By Joshua Ironside

Vocabulary Suggestions

fisher	fisherman	boat	cast	throw
net	multitude	deep	catch	many
launch	nothing	water	men	follow
me	astonished	haul	pull	gather
right	miracle	side	coin	money
inside	tribute			

Writing Ideas

- I would like to be a fisher of men because . . .
- A fisher of men is . . .
- Imagine you saw one of Jesus' miracles about fish. Which one would you most like to have seen? What would you have done and said after seeing the miracle?
- My name is Simon, and I had just spent whole night fishing without catching a fish when . . .

IF9521 3-D Christian Story Start

IF9521 3-D Christian Story Starters

Psalm 23; John 10:1–21

Teacher Preparation for Each Student:

- Duplicate the shepherd patterns (pages 44 and 45) on white construction paper.
- Cut writing paper into 3½-by-4-inch sheets, leaving an unlined space of one-half inch at the top.

Student Instructions:

1. Cut out all pieces along the solid outer lines.
2. Fold the side sections of the upper body toward the center along the dotted lines.

3. Glue the shepherd's head to the tab at the top of the body.
4. Glue the belt pieces along the bottom of the front flaps.
5. Glue the tabs on the arms to the back of the body.

6. Copy your story on the writing paper.
7. Put the story pages in order, placing the first page on top.
8. Open the flaps. Place the story pages inside. Then, staple them to the body along the top edge.
9. Write the story title and your name on the inside flaps.
10. Close the flaps. Color the shepherd.

Vocabulary Suggestions

shepherd	sheep	flock	tend	watch
care	know	call	name	follow
stranger	voice	pastures	water	leads
rod	staff	robber	save	good
kind	gentle	calm	upset	life

Writing Ideas

- Jesus is the Good Shepherd because . . .
- A Shepherd Loves His Sheep
- Sheep follow the shepherd because . . .

- List the qualities a good shepherd must have.
- A Shepherd's Job
- Write about how Jesus is your shepherd.

Tab

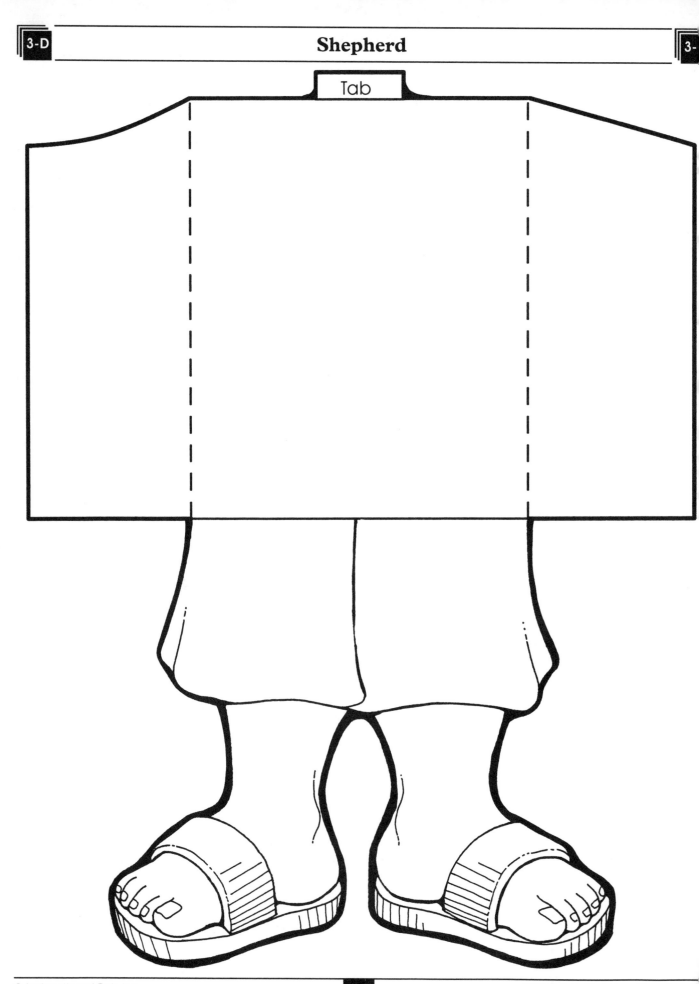

belt

Tab

Tab

belt

Twelve Apostles

Matthew 10; Mark 3:14–19; Luke 6:12–16; Acts 3; Acts 5:12–42

Teacher Preparation for Each Student:

- Make a copy of the Twelve Apostles patterns (pages 47 and 48) on white construction paper.
- Cut writing paper into 4-by-8½-inch sheets.

Student Instructions:

1. Color all of the pictures. Then, cut out each picture along the solid outer lines.

2. Cut slits indicated by solid lines.

3. Fold along the dotted lines.

4. Insert the slits of the four apostles section (A) into the A slits of the background scene. Fold over the tabs and glue in place. Insert the three apostles section (B) into the B slits. Fold over the tabs and glue in place.

5. Insert the three apostles section (C) into the C slits in front of the other three apostles section. Fold over the tabs and glue them in place.

6. Fold a 9-by-12-inch sheet of colored construction paper in half for a cover. Open it.

7. Glue the background piece to the inside of the top half, placing the bottom edge along the fold line.

8. Copy your story on the writing paper.

9. Arrange the pages in order, with the first page of the story on top.

10. Glue the last page of the story to the construction paper below the three-dimensional picture. Place the other pages on top of the last page and staple them all to the book along the left side.

11. As you fold the top down, gently pull the pop-out section to one side.

12. Write your story title and your name on the front cover.

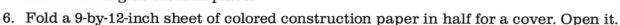

Vocabulary Suggestions

Jesus	God	pray	evil	apostles
twelve	power	cast out	rid	disciples
spirits	heal	sickness	disease	Simon (Peter)
Andrew	James	John	Philip	Bartholomew
Thomas	Matthew	James	Judas	Simon the Zealot
travel	teach	preach	people	Thaddaeus
hear	words	taught	follow	followers
listen	betrayal	teachers		

Writing Ideas

- If I had been one of the twelve apostles, I would have . . .
- Write about the life of one of the twelve apostles.
- The Last Supper
- A good apostle/disciple is . . .
- The apostles performed miracles . .

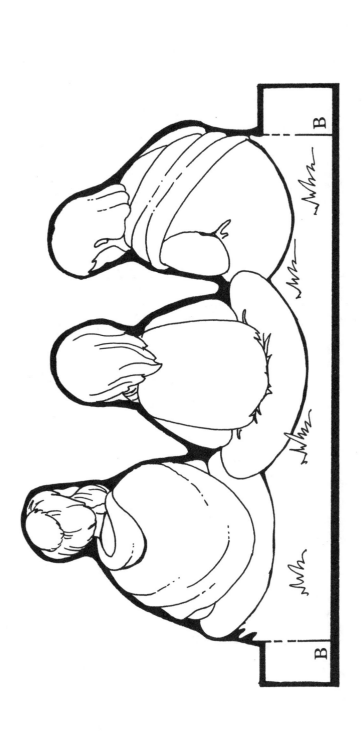

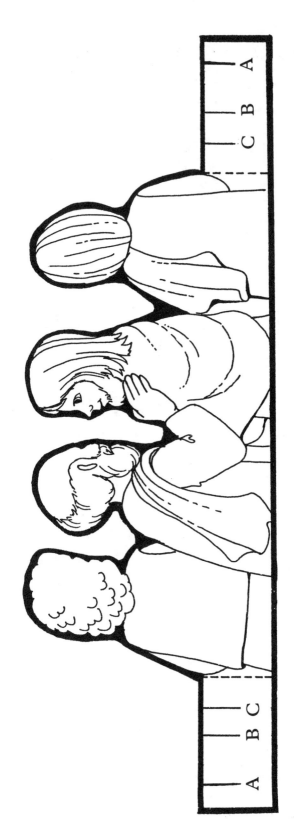

Matthew 18:1–6, 10; 19:13–15; Mark 9:36–37, 10:13–16; Luke 18:15–17

Teacher Preparation for Each Student:

- Duplicate the Jesus and Children background scene (page 51) on white construction paper.
- Make a copy of the children (page 50) on white construction paper.
- Cut writing paper into 4-by-8-inch sheets.

Student Instructions:

1. Color the background scene and children.
2. Cut out the children and background scene along the solid outer lines.
3. Fold the Jesus and Children background scene in half along the dotted line so that the scene is showing.
4. Cut slits indicated by solid lines.
5. Open. Then, as you fold the top section down, gently push the pop-out tabs inward.
6. Open. Glue the children to the front of the pop-out tabs.
7. Copy your story on the writing paper.
8. Arrange your story pages in order with the first page on top.
9. Glue the last page of your story in the space below the pop-out scene.
10. Place the other pages of your story on top of the last page and staple together along the left side.
11. Fold a 9-by-12-inch sheet of colored construction paper in half. Glue it to the back of the pop-out page, matching the fold lines. Do not glue the pop-out sections.
12. Close the book. Write your story title and your name on the front cover.

Vocabulary Suggestions

allow	come	forbid	praise	child
little ones	believe	trust	innocent	receive
trusting	hold	arms	touch	love
hands	God	Jesus	truthful	teach
kind	gentle	learn	listening	pure
hear	bless	heart	teachings	speak
kingdom	heaven			

Writing Ideas

- If Jesus were to hold me on his lap, I would . . .
- I believe in Jesus because . . .
- Jesus Loves and Blesses All Children
- How Jesus Protects Children

Tab   **Tab**   **Tab**

Matthew 14:22–33

Teacher Preparation for Each Student:

- Make a copy of the Peter Walks on Water patterns (pages 53 and 54) on white construction paper.
- Cut writing paper into 4-by-8½-inch sheets.

Student Instructions

1. Color all of the pictures. Then, cut out each picture along the solid outer lines.
2. Cut slits indicated by solid lines.
3. Fold along the dotted lines.
4. Insert the slits of the Jesus section (A) into the A slits on the background scene. Fold over the tabs and glue in place.
5. Insert the Peter section (B) into the B slits on the Jesus section. Fold over the tabs and glue in place.
6. Insert the water section (C) into the C slits on the Jesus section. Fold over the tabs and glue in place.
7. Fold a 9-by-12-inch sheet of colored construction paper in half for a cover. Open it.
8. Glue the background piece to the inside of the top half of the cover, placing that the bottom edge along the fold line.
9. Copy your story on the writing paper.
10. Arrange the pages in order with the first page of the story on top.
11. Glue the last page of the story to the construction paper below the three-dimensional picture. Place the other pages on top and staple to the book along the left side.

The Miracle of the Fish

By Joshua Ironside

12. As you fold the top down, gently pull the pop-out section to one side.
13. Write the story title and your name on the front cover.

Vocabulary Suggestions

Peter	Jesus	walk	water	boat
waves	wind	saw	spirit	fear
afraid	sink	save	hand	caught
faith	doubt	believe	trust	happy
ceased	Son	God		

Writing Ideas

- Sometimes when I am afraid, I think of Peter walking on the water . . .
- Imagine you were Peter. Describe your thoughts as you walked across the water to Jesus.

- Having faith in Jesus means . . .
- Wind splashed waves against the boat, and I prayed that Jesus . . .

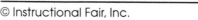

Water to Wine, John 2:1–11; Fig Tree, Matthew 21:18–22; Storm Calmed, Matthew 8:23–27; Miracle at the Pool, John 5:1–15; Lazarus, John 11:1–44; Ten Lepers, Luke 17:11–19

Teacher Preparation for Each Student:

- Duplicate the Jesus patterns (pages 56 and 57) on white construction paper.
- Cut writing paper into 3¾-by-4-inch sheets.

Student Instructions:

1. Cut out all pieces along the solid outer lines.
2. Fold the side sections of the upper body along the dotted lines.

3. Glue Jesus' head to the tab at the top of the body.
4. Glue the belt pieces along the bottom of the front flaps.

5. Glue the tabs on the arms to the back of the body.

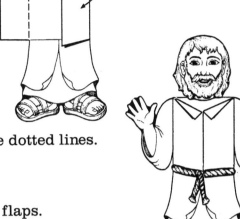

6. Copy your story on the writing paper.
7. Put the story pages in order, placing the first page on top.
8. Open the flaps. Place the story pages inside. Then, staple them to the body just below the neck.
9. Write the story title and your name on the inside flaps.
10. Close the flaps. Color Jesus.

Vocabulary Suggestions

loving	gentle	kind	leader	tree
performed	miracles	spoke	water	wine
withered	caring	glory	calm	people
lessons	asleep	little	faith	storm
marvelled	moving	pool	thanks	rise
rebuked	cleansed	heal	walk	dead
Lazarus	believed	see	mercy	show
yourselves	priests	sick	help	life

Writing Ideas

- Choose one of Jesus' miracles. Write about the miracle, why he performed it, and the effect it had on the people who witnessed it.

- It would be a miracle if Jesus . . .

- Write about an event in Jesus' life.
- Write a special prayer to Jesus as if you were one of the healed people.

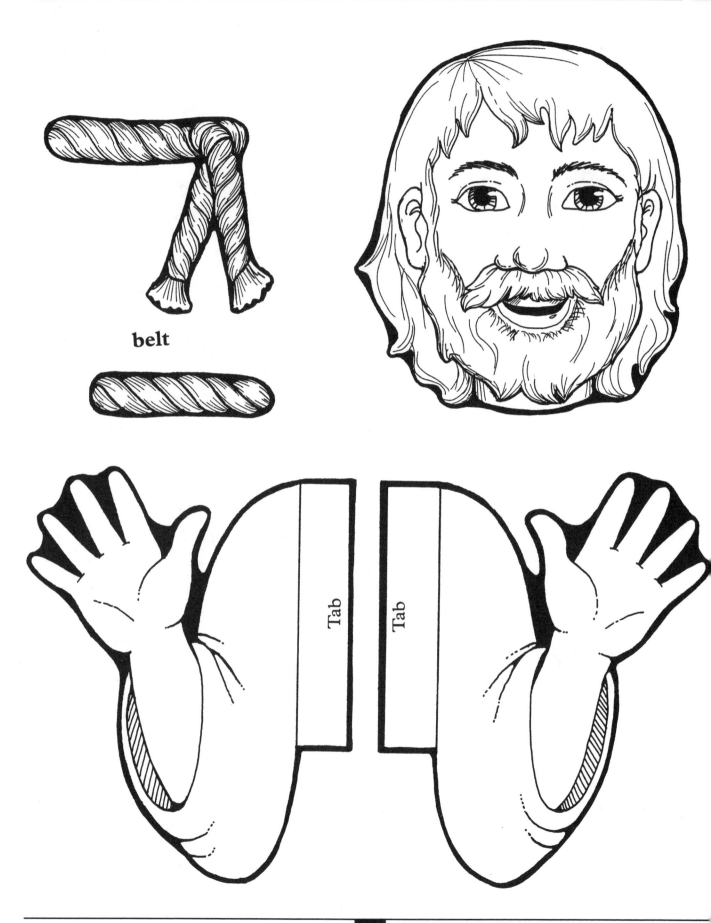

belt

Tab

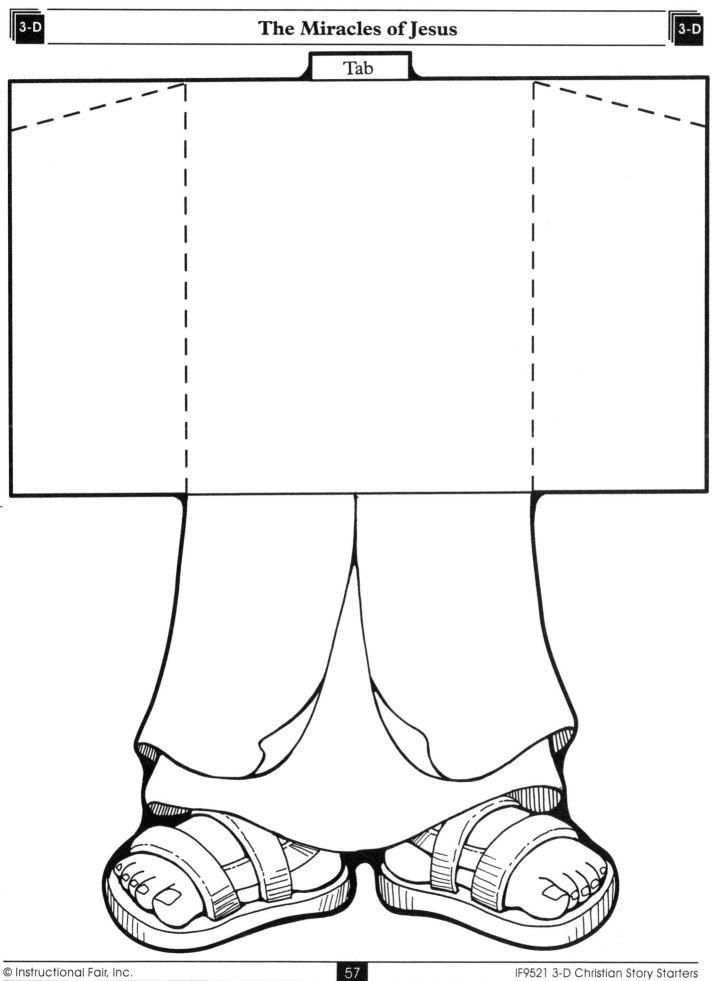

Mark 8:34; Luke 9:23; Matthew 27:32–50; Mark 15:21–39; Luke 23:26–46; John 19:17–30

Teacher Preparation for Each Student:

- Duplicate the stained glass window background scene, the cross, and the tab patterns (page 59) on white construction paper.
- Cut writing paper into 5-by-8-inch sheets.

Student Instructions:

1. Color the stained glass window scene and the cross.
2. Cut out the stained glass window scene, the cross, and the tab along the solid outer lines.
3. Fold the tab accordion-style along the dotted lines.
4. Glue the cross to one end of the tab.
5. Glue the loose end of the tab to the center of the stained glass window scene.

6. Fold a sheet of 9-by-12-inch colored construction paper in half. Open and glue the picture to the inside of the top half of the construction paper, placing the bottom edge along the fold line.
7. Copy your story on the writing paper.
8. Arrange your story pages in order, placing the first page on top.

9. Glue the last page of your story on the bottom half of the construction paper, below the stained glass scene.
10. Place the other pages on top and staple along the left side.
11. Close the book. Write the story title and your name on the front cover.

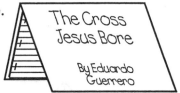

The Cross
Jesus Bore

By Eduardo
Guerrero

Vocabulary Suggestions

Easter	Jews	rises	garments	resurrection
Jesus	save	sinners	forgive	crucifixion
sins	cross	hope	sadness	rejoicing
king	carry	thieves	darkness	Golgotha
bear	robbers	chief priests	kingdom	

Writing Ideas

- When I look at the cross, I . . .
- On Easter Sunday, we . . .
- Why Christ Died for Our Sins

- A cross stands for . . .
- The Most Beautiful Cross in the World
- I was there on the day Jesus . . .

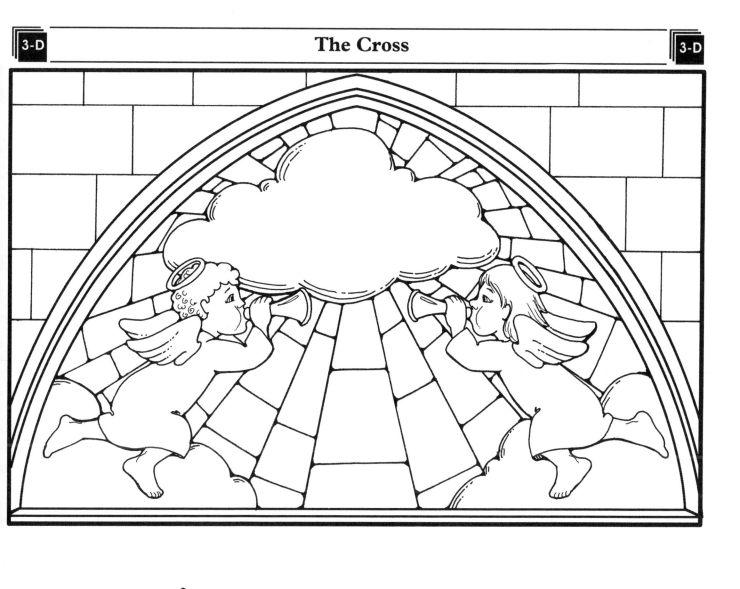

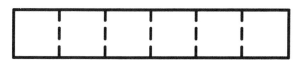

The Empty Tomb

Matthew 27:54–66, 28:1–8; Mark 15:39–47, 16:1–8; Luke 23:49–56, 24:1–12; John 19:38–42, 20:1–18

Teacher Preparation for Each Student:

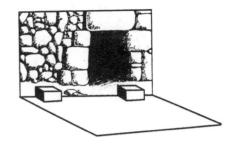

- Duplicate the tomb background scene (page 61) on white construction paper.
- Make a copy of the boulder and Mary (page 62) on white construction paper.
- Cut writing paper into 4-by-8-inch sheets.

Student Instructions:

1. Color the tomb background scene, the boulder, and Mary.
2. Cut out the boulder, Mary, and the tomb scene along the solid outer lines.
3. Fold the tomb scene in half along the dotted line so that the scene is showing.
4. Cut slits indicated by solid lines.
5. Open. Then, as you fold the top section down, gently push the pop-out tabs inward.

6. Open. Glue the boulder to tab A and Mary to tab B on the front of the pop-out tabs.
7. Copy your story on the writing paper.
8. Arrange your story pages in order, placing the first page on top.
9. Glue the last page of your story in the space below the pop-out scene.
10. Place the other pages of your story on top of the last page and staple together along the left side.
11. Fold a 9-by-12-inch sheet of colored construction paper in half to make a cover. Glue it to the back of the pop-out page, matching the fold lines. Do not glue the pop-out sections.
12. Close the book. Write the story title and your name on the front cover.

What Mary Didn't Find
By Rameen Zarrinnaal

Vocabulary Suggestions

burial	empty	carved	rock	tomb
guarding	Pilate	Jesus	Mary	centurions
Sabbath	fear	guard	risen	earthquake
body	linen	clothes	saw	believed
secured	stone	dead	angel	resurrection
joy	disciples	tell	heaven	Joseph of Arimathaea

Writing Ideas

- If I had been at the tomb when the angel came, I . . .
- Christ Is Alive
- Where Is Jesus?

- Imagine you were a soldier who watched over Jesus' tomb. Write your thoughts as you watched the angel remove the stone from the tomb.
- Have Faith in God's Words

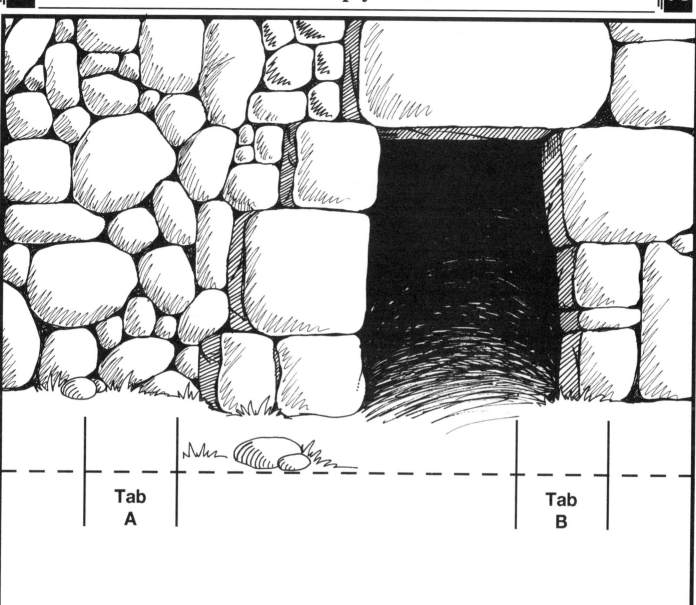

**Tab
A**

**Tab
B**

A

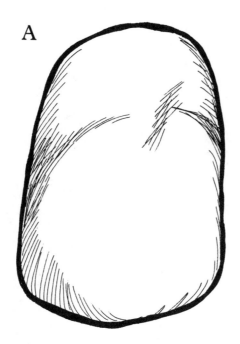

B

Jesus Rises into Heaven

Mark 16:19–20; Luke 24:50–52; Acts 1:3–11

Teacher Preparation for Each Student:

- Make a copy of Jesus and the heaven and angels background scene (page 64) on white construction paper.

- Cut writing paper into 5-by-8-inch sheets.

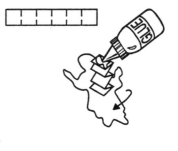

Student Instructions:

1. Color the heaven background scene and Jesus.

2. Cut out Jesus, the heaven background scene, and the tab along the solid outer lines.

3. Fold the tab accordion-style along the dotted lines.

4. Glue Jesus to one end of the tab.

5. Glue the other end of the tab to the background scene.

6. Fold a sheet of 9-by-12-inch colored construction paper in half for a cover. Open it.

7. Glue the background piece to the inside of the top half of the construction paper.

8. Copy your story on the writing paper.

9. Arrange your story pages in order, placing the first page on top.

10. Glue the last page of your story on the bottom half of the construction paper, below the heaven scene.

11. Place the other pages on top and staple along the left side.

12. Close the book. Write the story title and your name on the front cover.

Jesus In Heaven

By Kelly O'Brien

Vocabulary Suggestions

Jesus	disciples	heaven	rise	taken
earth	blessed	lifted	cloud	hid
God	stared	upward	joy	hand
right	praising	worship	sat	two
men	dressed	white	come	back

Writing Ideas

- As Jesus rose into heaven . . .
- The Day Christ Returns
- Christ Is Always with Us
- A Heavenly Sight

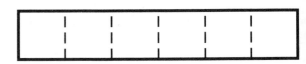

IF9521 3-D Christian Story Starter